A Giant Never Dies

Poems for Children and their Parents

Gabriel Fitzmaurice

Illustrated by
Sandra Elswieser

POOLBEG
FOR CHILDREN

Published 2002
Poolbeg Press Ltd.
123 Grange Hill, Baldoyle,
Dublin 13, Ireland
Email: poolbeg@poolbeg.com

1 3 5 7 9 10 8 6 4 2

A catalogue record for this book is available from the British Library.

ISBN 1-84223-009-3

Cover designed by Steven Hope
Illustrations by Sandra Elswieser
Typeset by Patricia Hope in Stone Serif 10.5/14
Printed by
Cox & Wyman
Reading, Berkshire

www.poolbeg.com

Biography

Gabriel Fitzmaurice was born, in 1952, in Moyvane, Co. Kerry where he still lives. He teaches in the local National School. He is author of more than thirty books, including poetry in English and Irish, children's verse in English and Irish, translations from the Irish, essays, and collections of songs and ballads. Described as "Ireland's favourite poet for children" (Claire Ranson, *Best Books*), he frequently broadcasts on RTE radio and television and local radio stations on education and the arts.

For Nessa and John who keep me young

Contents

Saturday Night

Rub-a-dub-dub
Look what's in the tub!
Little Boy Blue with his horn,
Little Bo Peep
Who's lost all her sheep
(No wonder she looks so forlorn);

Little Jack Horner
In from the corner,
Little Miss Muffet's there too –
It's Saturday night
And they're scrubbed till they're bright
By the Woman who Lives in the Shoe.

Therapy

I eat all my jumpers –
I just *love* the wool,
And though it looks silly
And not at all cool,

I love chewing my jumpers,
My reds, greens and blacks –
It's as good as a bottle
To help me relax!

I'm Not Your Friend

I'm not your friend,
You're a meany,
You threw pyjamas
On my head
Because I had
A teeny-weeny
Little sleep-out
In my bed.

I'm not your friend,
You're a fatso,
You ate my nuts
For Hallowe'en
And hid our witches'
Masks and hats. Oh
I think
That you're so mean.

I'm not your friend,
You're a bone face,
You threw pyjamas
On my head;
Now off you go
Back to your own space –
I'm going to play
With my dolls instead.

A Basser Bee

A basser bee, he bit me
And it was very sore;
If I could catch that basser bee,
He'd bite no more.

He wasn't humming in the flowers
Looking for his food –
He just flew up and bit me.
That basser is no good.

A Pleasure to Feed

I eat all my dinner,
I empty my plate
And count all the meat
And spuds that I ate.
I eat curry and chilli
And stir-fry and stew
And hairy fat bacon
And mackerel too.
I eat all around me
My Mammy once said,
But it's better to eat
Than to starve yourself dead
And my little brother's
A finicky weed
But everyone says
I'm a pleasure to feed.

In the Restaurant

"I want the meat what's in black stones.
Daddy, you get it for me?
I want the meat what's in black stones."
(Mussels, it turns out to be).

Dad gets her the meat what's in black stones;
She eats one, then strays on the floor –
"I no want the meat what's in black stones.
I no want it, Daddy, no more."

"Daddy, can I have an ice cream?
If you buy me one I will be good."
"No dear. You must eat your dinner;
Come on now and eat up your food."

"Daddy, can I have an ice cream?
Will you buy me one if I cry?
If I cry, Dad, can I have an ice cream?
Look! There's a tear in my eye."

"Come on, dear, and eat up your dinner
Before the meat in the black stones gets cold.
Come on, dear, and eat up your dinner –
You know that you're being bold."

"I hate this oul' place where we're eating,
I no like you, Dad, when you scold,
I want to go home to my Mammy,
You can only eat here if you're old."

First Day at School

The Babies begin
The Babies begin
The Babies begin school today
And their poor Mammies wait
Outside at the gate –
If only the Mammies could stay!

'Cos the Babies are small
And the Babies are cute
And Mammy must now say goodbye
And the Babies are happy
To go to Big School –
It's the Mammies this morning who cry.

The Babies begin
The Babies begin
The Babies begin school today
And I know if I'm good
And do all I should
I'll be asked to mind one at play.

The Babies begin
The Babies begin
The Babies begin school today
And their poor Mammies wait
Outside at the gate –
The house will be empty today.

The Parcel

My name for it was "parcel"
(Poo-poos in my pants),
And when you had to walk with it,
You made a kind of dance

With a wiggle and a waggle
And a sideways kind of glance
Going home to Mammy
With a parcel in your pants.

And all the village noticed
By the funny way you'd walk,
And you had to brave the gauntlet
Of the whistles, squeals and squawks;

And even your friends would tease you,
Hold their noses, cry "the stink!"
Till you got home to Mammy
And she'd wash you at the sink.

And she'd put you in new trousers
And advise you once again
To be sure and use the toilet
Before you went out with your friends.

8

Learning my figures,
There's one thing I hate –
Though I've tried and I've tried,
I can't make an 8.

I start at the top,
I turn and I twist
But 8 is a shape
Not made for my wrist

For no matter how hard
I weave and I wiggle,
My 8 is no more
Than a lopsided squiggle.

There's nothing left now
But to give up and cheat,
Put an "O" on an "O"
And pretend it's an 8;

And though it looks gammy
'Twill just have to do
Until I get bigger
And can write, Dad, like you.

Brum

Brum has lasted
Nine long years,
Kept away
My night-time fears.

While others cry
And suck their thumb,
All I need do
Is snuggle Brum.

Brum's been with me
All my life,
He'll never die
While I'm alive.

And though he's tattered,
Frayed and torn,
Every night
He keeps me warm,

My baby blanket –
Now you see!
I love Brum
And Brum loves me.

My Nose

Oh! I don't feel very good
About my nose
And, to make it worse,
Mammy says it snores.

It's long and thin
And at the end it curls up
And Daddy's always joking me
To take my nose out of the cup
When I drink tea.

Oh, I wish I had a different –
A film star kind of nose –
Because the nose I'm stuck with
Is not the one I'd choose.

But Daddy says it suits me,
That my nose is very *ME*,
And I don't think he's joking
But I don't agree.

I HATE MY NOSE!

Magic and Missy

Magic and Missy
Came from Tralee –
Magic for John-John
And Missy for me.

Missy's my rabbit,
She's cuddly and brown
And I pick her up
When I'm feeling down.

I hug her and rub her
So soft on my hand,
Just me and my Missy
Till everything's grand

'Cos I love my Missy
And Missy loves me –
Every day is like Christmas
Since she came from Tralee!

My Dog

His tongue hangs out when he is hot
And when he runs you see his bottom,
His tail straight up and waving 'round,
His four feet hardly touch the ground
As he runs before us up the drive
Barking, glad to be alive
So excited he does his wee.
I love him and he loves me,
My dog.

Animal Acrostics

Labradors

Labradors
Are
Big and friendly. They
Run to you
And jump up on you, or lie
Down
On the ground, belly-up for a
Rub.
Sit, boy! Sit!

Cats

Cats
Are able
To
Swim (but are the opposite of water).

Mice

Mice are the
Innocent victims of
Cheese-lust and their own
Endeavour.

Budgies

Budgies don't
Understand the
Daft things they say –
Gabbling
Imitators of
Every
Sound they hear.

Monkeys

Monkeys are like
Overactive kids who
Never
Know when to
Ease up,
Yet you wouldn't
Swap them for all the tea in China.

Cats

I thought cats were cuddly
Like Teddies in your bed
Until our cat brought home a mouse
And left the creature dead

On the step outside our kitchen door
And Daddy said that he
Was only trying to show us
How good a cat can be.

But the little mouse was broken,
On his nose a bead of blood –
And all this just to show us
A cat can kill real good.

He didn't want to eat him,
He just dropped him at the door –
Now I know things about cats
I didn't know before:

That no matter how you rear them
As pets in your own house,
A cat will, true to nature,
Always kill a mouse.

Spring Song

The birds are singing in the sky,
They are happy – so am I;
But, despite the joy they bring,
All the birds can do is sing.
So maybe it's just me that's glad
And birds sing, too, when they are sad.

The Bug and the Shoe

I'm the bug
And you're the shoe
And any day
I know that you

Could put your weight
Upon my back
And all you'd know
Is one small *crack* –

The sound you'd hear
Before I die.
Who are you?
And why am I?

Decimals

Dotsy things are decimals,
They're easy-peasy too –
Though sums are sometimes difficult,
Decimals I can do.

I add 'em up, subtract 'em,
Multiply, divide;
Boy, can I do decimals –
Every one I've tried!

They're not at all like other sums
Where you never know
What you're supposed to do with them –
I hate those sums. But, oh!

I love the dotsy decimals;
Just last week they were new,
But I know all about them now
'Cos decimals I can do!

Handwriting

When I was young, my writing
Was big and fat and tall
But now I'm ten, my writing
Is getting very small.

It's fine to have big writing
When you're learning how to write,
But writing like an Infant
When you're ten just isn't right.

So I hold my pencil tightly
And make my letters small;
I think teeny writing
Is the coolest kind of all
Though if it gets much smaller
It won't be seen at all!

The Cough

When I get things like reading
That I can't really do
I always cough a nervous cough.
Well, so would you

If you met words like mountains
Too high for you to climb
And just as you got near the top
You fell down every time;

If every time you met such words
Your brain turned black-and-blue,
Well let me tell you, smarty,
You'd be coughing too.

The English Lesson

I read 'bother' instead of *brother,*
'Thought' instead of *though,*
I read 'stared' instead of *started,*
'Now' instead of *know.*

Oh God! Some words are tricky
And reading them is hell
And just when I thought it could get no worse
We've got those words to spell.

A Hard Lesson

I got my Maths wrong –
Well, seven out of nine wrong anyway.
The teacher asked me to show him my copy.
I felt so ashamed,
I cried and cried.

The teacher told me to take it easy.
He smiled and said
I shouldn't be so hard on myself.
He asked me did I know anyone
Who never made a mistake?
I didn't.

But 'twas no good.
I can't stop crying.

Sometimes it's very hard to forgive yourself.

Bored

Summertime and I am bored –
Nothing to do all day;
I've played computers, watched TV,
There's no one here to play,

No one to swap stickers with,
I'm tired of playing pool
All alone in the sitting-room.
I wish I was in school.

What Would We Do Without Disney?

What would we do without Disney?
We'd have no Snow White or no Alice,
We'd have no Peter Pan or no Wendy,
No Aladdin seeking his Palace.

What did they do before Disney?
They all went off early to bed
And, happy to look at a favourite book,
They read and they read and they read.

Author, Author!

I made a book with writing –
Poems and stories too
With pictures at the bottom
And stuck the spine with glue.

Now I have my very own
Made-by-myself book
And all my friends come up to me
And ask me for a look.

The Book Fair

The Book Fair came to school today,
We pick a book and read away:
Harry Potter, Roald Dahl,
Bugs and Beasties, animals,
Books on science, history,
The Oxford Junior Dictionary,
Goosebumps, monsters, *Pokémon*,
Man. United, books with ROMs.
You pick this and I'll pick that,
We'll sit together, have a chat,
I'll show you and you'll show me
What we're reading, and then maybe
You'll swap yours and I'll swap mine
And 'round and 'round we'll go again
While at the case with a book of poems
Kristine's quite happy to read alone.

Scary Stories

A book is never scary –
Not like the films you see
If you're let into the cinema
Or on late-night TV.

A book is never scary
And you don't get such a shock
As you do when watching films,
'Cos when you read a book

You're reading at your own pace
And soak up all you need,
And even the surprises
Don't come at high speed.

A book is never scary –
When I turn out the light
After reading scary stories,
I can sleep at night.

Reading Harry Potter

Once we read him stories
That began with "Long Ago",
But when he got to reading age
Would he read them? No!

He's reading Harry Potter,
He reads it half the night
And he pleads for five more minutes
When Mam puts out the light.

He'd given up on reading –
A thing he did at school;
He thought that his computer games
Were the only thing that's cool,

But he's reading Harry Potter,
He reads it half the night
And he pleads for five more minutes
When Mam puts out the light

Till Mam in desperation
Went into bed with him
And read him *Harry Potter*
Right through to the end.

Now he's reading Harry Potter,
He reads it half the night
And he pleads for five more minutes
When Mam puts out the light.

So here's to *Harry Potter,*
The saviour of the book,
For once you hear his story
You're hooked!

He's reading Harry Potter,
He reads it half the night
And he pleads for five more minutes
When Mam puts out the light.

Sitting on the Throne

I'm into *Harry Potter*
(I can read him on my own),
And to steal a few more minutes,
I read him on the throne –

That's what we call the toilet;
I read there all alone,
And no one can disturb me
When I'm sitting on the throne.

I'm into *Harry Potter* –
I read here while I sit,
And no one can disturb me
Till I decide to quit!

Boiled Eggs

I love to eat a boiled egg
For you never know just how
The yolk will turn out – hard or soft;
You cap the egg – and now

You push the spoon into the egg
And by the way it slides
Deep into the fleshy bit
You know what's there inside –

A hard yolk, a soft yolk,
Or, if it jumps at you,
A runny yolk that leaves your hand
All slime and sticky goo.

Tomato Sandwiches

Soggy tomato sandwiches
Are the ones that I like best –
You can keep your biscuits,
Crackers and the rest.

I make them in the morning
Before I go to school
And when I've finished making them
I soak them in the pool

Of tomato juice upon the plate
So they go soft and pink –
They're soggy and they're juicy!
I really *really* think

That there's nothing in this world as nice
As a sandwich made this way –
And the best of all about it is
I'm having some today.

Bursting Pimples

Did you ever burst a pimple?
It doesn't hurt at all –
The white stuff shoots right out of it
To the mirror on the wall;

And then you get a tissue
To mop up bits of blood
And you flush it down the toilet
And it goes off with the flood.

And you polish up the mirror
To get rid of all the goo
And you flush *that* down the toilet
Too.

Oh I love bursting pimples!
It doesn't hurt at all
When all the bad inside you
Is splattered on the wall.

The Hidden Art

Making a fart
Is an art.

The wind that comes
To your behind
Has a mind of its own
And its mind
Is set on blowing
And the pressure
Keeps on growing.

So
To make for quiet release
You hold it softly,
Then you ease
It slowly out between your cheeks –
If you're lucky it won't leak,
And no one knows
You've made a fart.

That's why farting
Is an art.

The Forty Shades of Green

In Granda's time, he told me,
They'd no toilets anywhere –
They had to do their business
In the open air

In orchards, fields and gardens
Where they would not be seen
And that's the reason, Granda says,
Why Ireland is so green.

Riding on a Bus

I don't like riding on a bus –
I'm much too shy, there's too much fuss,
Children screaming, all that noise!
Why can't all the girls and boys
Just sit down, enjoy the ride?
But my friends are overjoyed
When they go off on a trip
Stocked with Coke and sweets and crisps
On a bus to anywhere.
They are happy. *They* don't care!
While *I* am sitting on my own
Wishing I could be at home
In peace and quiet, no fights, no fuss.
I don't like riding on a bus.

The Back of the Bus Gang

We're the back of the bus gang,
We're here to keep you out,
Say what you like about us
(That we're every kind of lout),

We're the back of the bus gang,
And you'll never qualify
To join the back of the bus gang
No matter how you try.

We're the back of the bus gang,
We're tougher than the rest;
To get into the back of the bus gang
There's no exam or test.

You're born a back of the bus kid,
The kind you'd call a lout,
But we're the back of the bus gang –
Brainy Boy, KEEP OUT!

Afraid

Isn't it amazing
How all these boys
Who'd pull you down,
Gouge your eyes
At football
And other games
Put their heads down
When called
To sing a song.

Oh yes!
They're OK
When they're out
On the field of play
'Cos out there
You're not alone,
But to sing here
On their own
They're afraid.

They've reputations to protect,
Reputations
That might be wrecked
If when singing
A little song
They broke down
And their mates laughed.
So they pretend
That singing is for sissies.

But they're afraid.

And all their bluster
And their bluff
Won't ever, *ever* be enough
To convince me.

'Cos they'd stay
Away from school
Rather than sing
And look a fool
In the music test.

That's the way
The world is made –
We all learn
To be afraid

If it's not singing
It's something else,
We're afraid
To be ourselves
And all our bluster
And our bluff,
All our hustle,
Huff and puff
Is just our very silly way
Of refusing every day
To be ourselves.

'Cos we're afraid.

Happy Endings

In all the stories in my book
That make me want to scream,
They all have happy endings –
The whole thing was a dream!

A dream that you wake up from;
But some things don't go away,
Some things that are bad by night
Are just as bad by day.

So give me no more stories
Of dreams that wake up well
While people starve, are massacred
And waking up is hell.

This Pain

Sometimes
Right in the middle of everything
I get sad.

I might be playing happily
With my friends,
Or watching television,
Or simply daydreaming
When I get sad.

There's nothing to be sad about,
I tell myself,
But I can't fool myself.
There's plenty.

Sure! *I'm* OK
But people die
Every day;
People starve,
Nations fight
And nothing I do
Will make it right

Because this pain's
Not mine alone –
It's the world's pain:
Pain for every child that cries,
Pain for every child that dies,

Pain for every man and woman
Who worry about the time that's coming;
Pain for every fish and fowl,
Pain for every animal,
Pain for every plant and tree,
The world's pain I feel in me.

And yet, this very sudden grief
Also is its own relief –
You don't feel different when it goes,
It's just the prayer inside you grows
Another inch, another mile;
You realize that all the while
You thought you were on your own
(No one suffers pain alone)
Your pain was prayer,
Your pain was good
'Cos pain is more
Than just a mood.
This pain.

The Terror of the Village

The terror of the village
And I just barely four,
The loudest, crossest, cheekiest,
I'd wheedle sups of por-

ter from the old men
Who had nothing more to do
Than nurse half-pints and fill me up
With tales that weren't true.

Like the one about the Barton Boy
(The Devil cut off his tongue
'Cos he wouldn't shut up talking);
Or the story of the young

Boy down in Tarbert
Who was born at age five
While I wondered was I born at all
And how I came alive.

I was found under a cabbage,
The old men told me then
And they'd pay me for saying curses
(I made up most of them).

The terror of the village
Who ran away from school
The very first day he went there
Was frightened most of all.

And the porter and the curses
Were really just a way
Of whistling through my terror –
Just like it is today.

And when I see The Menace,
The terror of the street,
Doing all that I did
(Now that I'm discreet),

I know what drives him to it,
Why a kid would make such show
Just like me, his teacher,
Forty years ago.

Uncle Timmy

You'd think my Uncle Timmy
Was related to a goat
'Cos when I showed it to him
He ate my five-pound-note;

At least he shoved it in his mouth
And chomped and squelched and chewed
But when I cried he took it out
And said 'twas yucky food.

And he had a beardy face –
He'd rub you, jowl by jowl,
His beard was like a porcupine
And you'd begin to howl

Until he'd let you go, and then
He'd laugh and set you free.
That was his way of playing.
But he got through to me

'Cos somewhere deep inside him
Was a child that loved to play
And five-pound-notes and porcupines
Were just his awkward way

Of telling me he loved me
And that is why I'd go
To visit him each evening
Long long long ago.

Mr Holes-In-His-Socks

He's too lazy to cut his own toenails
And so he gets holes in his socks –
He buys them all the same colour
And keeps the good ones in a box.

So when he wakes up in the morning,
Pulls on his socks, and his toe
Cuts a great gash like a razor,
Does it peep out all day in his shoe?

No! He hops across to his wardrobe
And goes to the odds 'n' ends box
And picks up the first sock he finds there
And again has a good pair of socks.

The Well

I heard it of a winter's night
In childhood, years ago
When tales were told to keep the cold
Outside with the wind and snow

How once upon a moonlit night
A piper passed this way
Coming from a *céilí*
In the parish of Athea

And as he walked he whistled
A tune, a merry tune
And the only other sound that night
Was howling at the moon.

He walked along the fairy path
Whistling his merry tune
When suddenly a darkness
Stole across the moon

And all the dogs fell silent
As he came upon the well
And a voice from the waters spoke to him
And this is what befell:

There's some call it glaucoma
And some the fairies' curse
For when he woke next morning
Beside the fairy bush

He was blind; and ever after
He would never tell
What the voice of the waters whispered
From the fairy well.

The fairies are no longer
And all their wanton harm,
And the well supplies fresh water
Piped up to a farm,

And when I ask the old man
Who told the tale to me
If he believes in fairies
He says, "I don't believe

In fairies"
And turns to face me then:
"No! I don't believe in fairies.
But I'm afraid of them."

My Favourite Place

There's nothing I like better
Than to curl up in bed,
The blankets tucked around me
Covering my head,

A book upon the pillow
And to read the morning long,
My head full of adventure.
I've trained Pokémon

And sailed away with Gulliver
To the land of Lilliput
And the voyage isn't over
When the book is shut;

For in your mind you travel
With the stories that you've read
Till the bed where you are reading
Is no longer just a bed

But a kind of magic carpet
Taking you away
To a land that, once you've entered,
You won't want to go away.

Keeping the Flies Off of Molly

for Nessa

When I was in the cradle
Happy as the day
I never talked in scribble.
The first thing I could say

      Was

I'm keeping the flies off of Molly
All the liveday-long,
Keeping the flies off of Molly
Singing a little song.

And when they packed me off to school
All those years ago
And the teacher asked me
Things I didn't know

      I'd say

I'm keeping the flies off of Molly
All the liveday-long,
Keeping the flies off of Molly
Singing a little song.

And now that I am old and shrunk
And any day to die,
Do I sit and sulk and scream
And cringe and carp and cry?

No!

I'm keeping the flies off of Molly
All the liveday-long,
Keeping the flies off of Molly
Singing a little song.
Keeping the flies off of Molly
Singing the same old song.

A Boston Notebook

for Berna Mann

1 Boston

We were flying to Boston
On an Aer Lingus plane
From an Ireland whose summer
Was riddled with rain.

We were leaving behind us
The summers we knew –
When we landed in Boston,
It was raining there too.

But that first time in Boston!
No need to explain –
On such an adventure
You'd put up with the rain.

2 A Kerry Kid in Boston

"Ensign X" he called himself,
Our Duck Tour guide today –
"X is short for excellent,"
Was the first I heard him say.

The Duck drove all 'round Boston's streets
But the best thing it could do
(It was an amphibious landing craft
From World War II)

Was go out on the river,
Then Ensign X invites
My sister to steer the Duck
Much to her delight.

He invited all the other kids,
And when I got to steer,
He asked my name, where I came from
And all about my gear –

My green-and-gold Kerry strip,
He asked me what it was –
When he heard 'twas Gaelic football
He smiled at me because

He said 'twas tough as anything,
And when the tour was through
He gave "A softball to the Kerryman –
A present from the crew!"

The crew was just himself of course,
But once again I'd scored –
When I wear my Kerry jersey,
It opens many doors!

3 At the Science Museum, Boston

Nessa bet three dollars
She wouldn't like this place –
She said that science was boring;
She wasn't into space

And other things she'd learned in school
And so she laid the bet –
But soon she found that science
Is as good as you will get.

First she rubbed the stuffed black bear,
And in the Omniplex
She saw an Imax movie,
And then she saw T-Rex –

Forty-two by thirteen feet
(The museum named it "Sue"),
Sixty-seven million years
Old – take a year or two!

And then the electricity –
A man inside a cage
Made an electric thunderstorm
And how the lightning raged.

And she got to make some lightning too
On a Van de Graaff Lightning Ball –
Fancy making lightning
By spinning a little wheel!

There were moon particles on display,
A meteorite from Mars,
An Apollo command spaceship;
But what she preferred by far

Was the room with the computers –
One took her photograph
And printed it in colour.
Nessa had to laugh –

She hadn't known that science
Could ever be such fun.
When I asked if we still had that bet,
I knew that I had won!

4 FAO Schwarz

We had time to kill in Boston
So we went to see the shops
When suddenly we came upon
FAO Schwarz.

There was everything you could wish for there,
Cuddly bears and toys,
Lego, Duplo, board games –
A kiddies' paradise;

Electronic games and Barbies,
Planes, remote control,
Hoops and ropes and wooden blocks,
Books and videos;

Soccer, baseball, volleyball,
Puppets, bouncing balls,
T-shirts, robots, art and sweets –
I could have bought them all!

I had a load of dollars
In my wallet I could spend,
But I wanted to keep my money
And bought nothing in the end.

But Dad became a kid again,
And when he left the store
He'd bought a bag of children's books
(Some he'd read before) –

That's what the Schwarz store did to Dad –
Though he didn't go in to buy,
He ends up with a bag of books
And I with not one toy!

5 In Fenway Park

It wasn't like Old Trafford
And it wasn't like Croke Park –
This is the Boston Red Sox,
This is Fenway Park.

Underneath the stadium
Was like a fast-food mall,
And this is the very first time
I've ever seen baseball.

There were hot dogs there and pizza –
You could eat them in the stand,
And they sang their national anthem
Like we do in Ireland –

'Twas a bit like karaoke
With the words up on the screen,
Then the display up there changes
To a lineout of the teams.

There were people drinking cola,
There were people drinking beer;
The baseball was exciting
Full of gasps and cheers;

But I didn't understand it
For I don't know this game
So I drank my Coke and ate hot dogs
And watched it just the same.

The game went on for hours
Till after it was dark,
But at least I had a picnic
Tonight in Fenway Park!

6 A Phone-y Incident

I ring the operator
To get my Irish code –
America's not Europe
So the code I have's no good.

She asks me what's the city –
I can hardly say "Moyvane"
(Moyvane is not a city),
But she's American

So she asks me "What's the city?",
I say "The code is 068,
There's no city in my county –
It's not the United States".

But she asks me what's the city –
Alas, what can I do
But tell her it's a village.
And still I can't get through

To the woman at the other end
Never mind get through to home
So I thank her for her trouble
And put down the telephone.

7 In The Children's Museum, Boston

The Galway girl in the kids' museum
Asked where we came from –
She'd seen my Kerry jersey
And hoped we were from home.

She'd been in Boston for a year
And worked on her day off
In the kids' museum,
And she was speaking of

The time she spent in Boston
And her home in "Carraroe" –
Dad spoke to her in Irish
And it wasn't for the show

For there they speak in Irish –
That language is her own,
And here in the heart of Boston
For a moment she was home.

8 Making Bubbles in the Children's Museum, Boston

The person who thought up this place
Must have known a kid like me –
A place where children rule OK,
A place you can be free.

I framed a bubble, stretched a bubble,
Made a bubble dome –
You could wet the place with bubbles here
Which you can't do at home.

For in the kids' museum
The children rule OK –
And though I'm slightly old for this,
I could have stayed all day.

9 In The Public Gardens, Boston

Under a willow
In the Gardens today
While some were in Swan boats
And others at play,

I could feel in its shelter
My own dappled hush
While the city around me
Flashed by in a rush.

Under the willow
(My favourite tree)
I could feel here a something
I know is not me;

For under the ground
To the top of the tree
Is something much older
Than I'll ever be –

Something much older
That I can but feel
And though I can't name it,
I know that it's real.

10 Jamaica Pond

The old man in Jamaica Plain
Sits quietly by the pond,
Feeds the geese and goslings,
The pigeons, ducks and swans.

He sits there like St Francis,
Friend to all the birds
With a bag of breadcrumbs.
This is where no words

Complicate the giving:
They eat out of his hand
In a world only a bird-man
Will wholly understand.

11 Leaving Boston

The man at the Curbside Check-In
Said "This bag is overweight";
He said if we took care of him
He'd check it through the gate.

We paid of course – we're foreign here –
But when we told our friend
Who'd driven us to the airport,
She knew that we'd been conned –

He'd conned us into bribing him,
She was going to complain;
We wanted no such trouble
On our way out to the 'plane.

But just before we parted
And wished each other luck
She swore that before we were in the air
She'd get our twenty bucks.

12 Goodbye America!

So this has been America
As not seen on TV,
A place where you work very hard,
Drink coffee and iced tea;

Where you go to bed so early
And get up early too;
A place where you can't loiter
Except you're in a queue;

A place I thought where people
Were brash and often rude,
But the ones I met were friendly
And I just *love* their food;

A place I found where kids like me
Have little space to play
Not like at home in Kerry.
But it's *great* for a holiday!

A Giant Never Dies

i.m. Michael Hennessy of Moyvane and Ballyduff

"I come from sweet Knockauling,
John Bradley is my name
And I'm the king of hurlers
For hurling is my game."

So sang young John Bradley
As he dashed from the TV
His head full of hurling,
Great deeds and bravery

On that Sunday in September,
All Ireland Hurling Day,
The All Ireland Final over;
He dashed outside to play

With a hurling stick and rubber ball,
He hurled on his own –
He'd no brothers or no sisters
And so he played alone

Whack! against the gable
Then run and leap and catch
Re-playing the All Ireland,
Making it his match.

And then, his mind-game over,
He ran in home to Dad
And they talked of hurling heroes
And the mighty games they played.

Dad told him of the exploits
Of Big Mick Hennessy
Who played football for Knockauling
And hurling for Ballylee;

And how once upon a Championship
He was called to play
In the local Football Final
And on that selfsame day

When the football match was over
He played for Ballylee
In the County Hurling Final
In the great Park of Tralee.

In the centre for Knockauling,
He scored five points that day
And when the match was over
He left the field of play,

No time to celebrate and lift
The cup of victory –
He dashed out to the hackney car
That would take him to Tralee
And changed Knockauling's colours
For the green of Ballylee.

Just in time for the second half,
His team a goal behind,
Big Mick Hennessy took the field
And hurled into the wind;

And when the game was over
He'd scored three goals to win
And thousands knew they'd never see
The likes of him again.

* * *

The time is some weeks later,
The place – the Park, Tralee,
The County Hurling Final,
Tullybeg and Ballylee.

John Bradley and his Daddy
Have travelled here this day,
A treat for young John's birthday –
Eleven years today.

The game is fast and factious,
And at half time they see
The men of forty years ago,
Knockane and Ballylee,

As thirty men in suits walk out,
The hurlers of that day
When Big Mick Hennessy showed to all
How the great can play;

And as his name is called out
Each man waves to the crowd
And at the name "Mick Hennessy"
The cheers are long and loud.

But young John Bradley's puzzled –
The man he sees out there
Is not as he imagined:
With glasses, thinning hair,

To young John he looks no different
To the other men
Standing out there on the field.
He realises then

That Mick Hennessy's a story
Of a giant with a ball
And what he sees there on the field
Is not a giant at all.

Yes, Mick Hennessy's a story –
One that will be told
When Big Mick is dead and gone
And young John Bradley's old.

For a giant lives in story
Among his people who
Believe in deeds of greatness
And honour all that's true.

Yes, Mick Hennessy's our story,
A giant with a ball
Who once upon a Championship
Won glory for us all.